ENDANGERED SPE

Fritz Eichenberg

ENDANGERED SPECIES

and Other Fables
with a Twist

PUBLISHERS, INC.   OWINGS MILLS   MARYLAND   1979

Frontispiece: "Private Nightmare"

Inquiries should be directed to
Stemmer House Publishers, Inc.
2627 Caves Road
Owings Mills, Maryland 21117

A Barbara Holdridge book
Printed and bound in the United States of America
First Edition

Library of Congress Cataloging in Publication Data
Eichenberg, Fritz, 1901-
    Endangered species, and other fables with a twist.

    I. Title.
PN6162.E34   769'.92'4   79–15247
ISBN 0–916144–42–9
ISBN 0–916144–43–7 pbk.

Contents

Preface by the Artist

As in any fable worth its name, the year, the date, often even the place, are immaterial.

Let's say: Once upon a time not so long ago—I spent a lonely Christmas in Rome, my favorite of all cities.

I was working away on a series of wood engravings of yet another difficult Dostoevsky—*A Raw Youth*. I had not only a raw time but a severe case of the blues on top of it, as is customary with me at that time of the year when the spirit of Christmas rides rampant and commercial, and drives you easily to drink—or worse.

The churchbells across the Piazza di Collegio Romano didn't help either; but in the nick of time some dear new friends took compassion on the lonely artist, picked me up bodily at the Palazzo Doria (where I occupied a modest apartment) and conveyed me through the maddening Christmas traffic to the country estate of a Roman friend and gentleman-photographer with the imposing name of Michelangelo Durazzo. Bless his hospitable soul—and Saint Peter's, who had seen to it that it was a balmy day. We sat outside on the green grass under the ancient olive trees, sipped country wine and waited for the dinner bell.

Our host had prepared a fabulous meal; I use that adjective advisedly. He had just chased away one of his many cats from a delicious smoked salmon hidden high up on a shelf for safety's sake. The goose smelled as inviting as it should, and we ate and drank and chattered like heathen until we were satiated.

A Christmas sun sent its blessing through the tall kitchen windows and we felt good and kind toward this world of ours.

But Michelangelo, the perfect host, wanted to make us feel even better.

"Would you like to hear some nice stories for dessert?" he asked. "Some fables, perhaps?"

"Sure!" we yelled, a little tipsily. "It would certainly help our digestion."

"Since we are sitting so comfortably and well fed inside, waiting perhaps for another guest to knock at the door, how about 'The Ant and the Cricket?'"

"Go right ahead!" we shouted in several different languages, being a somewhat mixed but erudite audience; and thinking, slightly blasé, that we knew the story anyhow.

"You may remember," Michelangelo began with a Cheshire-cat smile, "how the nasty ant had warned the playful cricket not to sing all summer but rather think of stocking up on groceries for the hard winter which was sure to come, and *not* to come whining and begging for a handout when the storms begin to howl.

"Well, you know crickets," said our host, waving his hands in good Roman fashion. "Ours sang to his heart's content all through the summer, while the ant, sweating and smirking, filled her pantry with all necessities of life, waiting for that knock at the door when the first snow began to fall.

Three times our host knocked on the table. "That was," he said, "what the ant had been waiting for. She opened the door a crack, ready to slam it in the face of what she hoped would be the woebegone little beggar.

"Surprise! What the ant saw was a splendidly attired cricket, replete with blonde wig, granny glasses, high-heeled shoes, a sparkling electric guitar slung around his shoulders—a perfect pinup of a rock star!"

Michelangelo paused, and took a sip to heighten the suspense. His audience was sitting up.

"The ant," he smiled, "forgot to close the door, even to close her mouth.

" 'What happened?' she gasped.

" 'Quite simple, man!' the cricket chirped.

" 'Sitting under a tree, singing my heart out, banging away at the guitar, who whizzes by in their golden Rolls Royce but the Living Dead. You know, man! Wow! They offered me a contract, five grand a stand.' " ("Figure that out in lira," Michelangelo said!)

" 'I am a smash!' yelled the cricket, 'I am on my way! For old times' sake come along with me to gay Paree!'

" 'Out of my sight!' shrieked the ant, shocked and disappointed. 'How dare you spoil a grand old fable! But when you get to gay Paree, for old times' sake, look up old man La Fontaine, the swindler, and twist his neck!' And she slammed the door."

We clapped our hands and raised our glasses in a toast to our host, to his goose and wine, to the spirit of Christmas—and to the unexpected twist of a well-known fable.

That was the spark that set me to thinking of polishing the old fables, giving them a new twist, and of inventing new ones to fit our times, and of composing them on wood to give them permanence; and finally, since no one else would do it, of writing "librettos" in blank verse for them, and letting text and image go out into the world together, looking for an audience which could either applaud or boo them.

My blues were over. With Watergate and Vietnam receding into history I moved from the Palazzo Doria back to the U.S.A., and in my little cottage on Nantucket began the parade of the woodblocks, good Swiss pear, week after week, until somewhere I had to stop.

Once you have started on this binge, fables have a way of dogging your steps—you see the beast in every human, yourself included, and wonder whom you prefer.

You open your daily paper, turn on the radio, or, God forbid, the Idiot Box, and there is ample fresh material for yet another set of fables—with plenty of twists. The subject of human follies seems inexhaustible.

According to old man Webster, *"The fable is a fictitious narrative intended to teach some moral truth or precept, in which animals and sometimes inanimate objects are represented as speakers and actors."* What was good enough for Webster is still good enough for me, although I am all for dusting off old definitions which have served their time.

By chance or foresight I got my little foot in the door a long time ago. Animals of all sorts were my early companions. Much of my free time, away from my hated school, I spent in the zoo, at the circus, at country fairs, later on horseback—and never without my sketchbook. Shy as I was, I felt a kinship with "dumb" animals which I missed in associating with my more articulate fellowmen—especially my Prussian drillmasters.

I craved affection, and my love for animals was always returned in full measure. While I sketched them they studied me. We met on the same wavelength, I passed inspection.

They yearned as much for freedom as I did. When I compared them with human beings, the latter usually came out second best.

Little did I realize in those early days that I had met all the models for my fables—I can draw them now by heart!

Over the ages they have afforded wonderful camouflage to critics of the imperfect society that we human beings created. This kind of storytelling must have begun in the dark caves of Altamira, as some of the wall paintings still seem to testify; on bas-reliefs in ancient Egypt (a gazelle playing chess with the lion); in pre-Christian India, written in Sanscrit in the *Panchatantra*'s Five Books; finding their way through the shadowy hands of Bidpai and Aesop; given permanence by anonymous writers, calligraphers, illuminators and printmakers; going through the minds, pens and brushes of a LaFontaine, a Calder and countless others—what a magnificent panoply of meaningful humor, hidden satire, bitter accusations that will continue "to teach some moral truths" to future generations.

One could also call the fable, in word and picture, a very effective way of avoiding libel suits. The fable is a matter of interpretation beyond the reach of the law; and the animals themselves, unfortunately, have no way of protesting. They have, of course, been libeled since the Fall—the Bible had something to do with it. Yet the snake, very often shown in the shape of a woman as a symbol of evil, is also shown biting its tail as a symbol of eternal life. In one of my favorite themes, "The Peaceable Kingdom" (Isaiah 11), the child is playing fearlessly with the snake, watched over by the lion and the ox, while the leopard lies peacefully with the lamb, and the wolf plays with the kid.

What is one to think of these contradictions? I have been reproached by fundamentalists and zoologists alike, and played the Devil's advocate by saying that these predators had taken a real liking to their herbivorous playmates, taken the pledge and become vegetarians.

Still, it's difficult to make a case for the snake, who even now is blamed for our expulsion from Paradise. On the other hand, the ox and the donkey have earned a place in our affections because they witnessed the birth of Christ, while the innocent pig, expelled by Christ from the possessed, is seen as a dirty glutton, and the goat as the very image of lust and the Devil himself.

Esthetics may play a role in that: The horse and the deer have forever been considered noble; the eagle and the lion so majestic that they are proudly shown on coats-of-arms. The dove, well-known for her sexual proclivities, stands now for peace and even for the Holy Ghost. But the wolf and the fox have always been persecuted as blood-thirsty and cunning creatures—even though they are now protected and praised by environmentalists.

Pity the poor fabulist, look with compassion and sympathy on the labors of the illustrator of fables, fighting his way through this jungle of contradictions and misconceptions, trying not to do an injustice to our furred and feathered friends by making them represent our own human villainies and prejudices.

One thing is sure: one can't approach the fable with the eye of cold rationality, or with the tools of a zoologist. The fable has achieved immunity by crossing the line into the territory of the myth, where it feels perfectly safe.

Perhaps one way of better understanding all of this would be to watch the artist at work in his little studio on the Island of Nantucket. Yes, he is working on his fables, but he is also receiving his messages from the life around him: a catbird talking to him, asking for a handout of raisins; a red-tailed hawk leisurely dismembering a tiny rabbit he has caught in the meadow; a garden snake wiggling into a mole hole; a ringtailed pheasant crossing the lawn, carefully looking for its mate; a deer guiding two wobbly fawns across the meadow to a hideout; a seagull with a broken foot landing on the chimney looking around for some easy food—all have a message for the artist and his fables.

He may walk along the empty beach some afternoon and discover a shark patroling the shallow water, keeping an eye on his observer; a tern dive-bombing the beachcomber to protect his little fledglings; driftwood and pebbles that assume life in the artist's hands. There is magic in the air, the wind, the land; the waves are the stuff that myth and fable are made of—if only you have eyes to see and ears to hear the whispered messages.

The artist has to respect the tools he works with—they have a nobility of their own, acquired over the many years of association. They will return the compliment and help the work along.

The material has to be of the best quality. The wood and graver being my most favorite medium, a lot of time goes into the proper selection. A tool is rarely discarded—if ever. It acquires a patina over the years, it has to be kept razor-sharp, treated like a beloved pet. The wood has to be properly aged, carefully glued together and planed, kept away like a child from extreme cold or heat.

Ink and paper have an affinity for each other, embrace each other. The proper inking and the pulling of the first proof are the moment of truth, sometimes elating, often disappointing or shattering—depending on one's expectations.

And so the work flows along, day after day, more or less harmoniously but steadily, as daily life with all its interruptions will permit.

And one day twenty-six prints are ready to go out into the cold world, for better or for worse, to stand on their own. What kind of reception they will get one never knows, but one hopes for the best. Suddenly they are in exhibitions here and there, traveling over the ocean, appearing in the pages of the *New York Times* or in a little paper devoted to a favorite cause, acquired by some print collection, or appearing—who knows?—in a book such as this one!

Peace Dale   *Fritz Eichenberg*
Rhode Island
May 1979

Introduction

"At this moment, we are willing to believe that there may be only half-a-dozen truly great illustrators in the world today. We are willing to believe that we could not name all of them. But we are willing to insist that, in any group of six illustrators who are to be called great, *Fritz Eichenberg must belong." (Heritage Press, on the occasion of publication of* The Brothers Karamazov)

Perhaps there is a problem with that word "illustrator." It sounds as if someone is trying to enhance something that is already there. Actually Fritz Eichenberg's work does not so much "enhance" as it "embodies" a text. The word of the text is made flesh, as it is in the work of Rembrandt and Holbein and Dürer.

Fritz Eichenberg was born in Cologne, Germany, where he lived through the horrors of the first World War. He studied graphic arts in Leipzig, and then went to Berlin to become a staff artist and reporter of a big newspaper chain. Like Goya and Daumier before him, Eichenberg began doing caricatures of some of the contemporary political figures, including the rising führer, Adolf Hitler. When the native soil became too hot, at the age of thirty-two, Eichenberg left Europe for the "New Continent."

After a difficult start during the Great Depression in the U.S.A., Eichenberg turned to books, printmaking and teaching, illustrating more than one hundred volumes, many of them for the Limited Editions Club and The Heritage Press. The list of these books reads like a history of Western literature—Shakespeare, Goethe, Tolstoy, Dostoevsky, Swift, the Brontës, Poe, Dylan Thomas, and most recently, the wry good sense of Erasmus in his *Praise of Folly,* and Grimmelshausen, *The Adventurous Simplicissimus,* the first great novel of the Thirty Years War.

Eichenberg's major work is associated with the nineteenth-century Russian novelists—Tolstoy and Dostoevsky especially. And these great novelists range over the subjects of war, murder, suicide, exile, executions, adultery and madness. This does not sound like particularly romantic material—but then again, it is romantic in the very sharpest sense of the word—because in both Tolstoy and Dostoevsky, the heartfelt gesture of the soul towards salvation is in deadly earnest, and arises out of the reality of human emotion confronting the terrible contradictions of existence.

How to describe the style of Eichenberg's work? One would have to go back to some of Blake's annotations, to Sir Joshua Reynolds' Discourses. Blake insists on the importance of the line in drawing—for him, blurred work is blurred vision: Broken Colours & Broken Lines & Broken Masses are Equally Subversive of the Sublime. For him, "Execution is the Chariot of Genius"—Without Minute Neatness of Execution the Sublime Cannot Exist! Grandness of Ideas is Founded on Precision of Ideas.

One feels this insistence on care and neatness of execution in Fritz Eichenberg's work. His line is clear, strong, and precise—almost cartoon-like in caricature, grotesque in torment, surreal in exaltation—yet always straightforward, exact and sensuous. It is a living line, one that has been won.

Eichenberg's first critical success was *Crime and Punishment,* and it is not hard to see why. His wood engravings are a testament to man's eternal struggle with the forces of darkness. There are the wizened eyes of the landlady peeking through the half-open door. There is Raskolnikov's fever dream of the brutal beating of the little horse. And there is the extraordinary print of Raskolnikov standing by the door, ax in hand, waiting in terrible anticipation. All of the figures of the novel seem to be propelled by some violent inner energy that is both menacing and redemptive.

Then there is Tolstoy's *War and Peace*—that colossal encyclopedic work which is unified by the great action of Russia's awakening national spirit. Eichenberg has done brush drawings of Tolstoy barefoot on the grass, drawings of armies on the march, of Napoleon surveying the wreckage of his war, drawings of the wretched prisoners, and always, there are drawings of Pierre, who stands at the heart and soul of this great endless novel.

The Brothers Karamazov has nearly fifty lithographs which create the world of this demonic, possessed and impassioned family. There are Alyosha as a young boy, and Fyodor Pavlovich, the old Buffoon, kneeling before the aged Father Zosima. There is a remarkable print of The Boy Who Threw the Stone, standing on a bridge, his small body alive with outrage and fierce defiance. And there is the master print of the stern Inquisitor, forlorn of figure, and over the darkness of the scene there is the superimposed face of the living Christ. There are other prints—the Orgy, the Madness of Dmitri, The Mystery of the Earth, The Imp, Gentlemen of the Jury—all of them filled with a sense of the contradictions of existence.

Other high points in the artist's work are *Resurrection,* Tolstoy's *J'accuse* of the Tsarist penal system, with wood engravings showing with authenticity the trial, the journey to Siberia, the jails and exile stations—grim images backed by a close study of source material!—and Turgenev's *Fathers and Sons,* an infinite description in wood engraving of Russian country life and the clash of two generations, and Dostoevsky's *The Idiot,* in which two prints especially stand out: the bareheaded man on the scaffold of the guillotine, confronting the crucifix—and Ippolit, standing in an open doorway, his left hand raised with an empty glass, his right hand holding a revolver to his head.

There is Emily Brontë's *Wuthering Heights,* showing in black and white the brooding English countryside, mad dogs and crags and granges—and the terrible scene of Heathcliff digging at Catherine's grave—companion volume to Charlotte Brontë's *Jane Eyre,* showing the terrors of the orphanage, the tragedy of Mr. Rochester, his mad wife, and Jane's reunion with her blinded master.

In a lighter vein, there came into being the engravings for *Gulliver's Travels* and Goethe's *Reynard the Fox,* filled with fabled animals.

These are all haunting images which float in the mind long after one sets the books aside.

And still one goes back to the books which contain these prints, again and again. And one also senses here a great love for fine bookmaking, as an end in itself—the love of holding good books, the love of looking through them, the love of keeping them close to oneself, as if they were testaments.

If this is "illustration," it is illustration of the highest order—for Eichenberg's work is an egoless art, so subsumed is it in its subject matter. Heathcliff and Raskolnikov, Alyosha and Dmitri, Natasha and Pierre stand there forever in their terrible contradictions.

In the small pamphlet *Art and Faith,* published in 1952 by Pendle Hill (#68), Fritz Eichenberg describes how the artist must enter into this visionary experience of the work: "Creative man is lonely in his labors. No midwife can assist him, no power can help him along, except for the one great source of strength from which he receives his commands. When Händel wrote the "Messiah," he fervently prayed every morning to Him to whom he had dedicated it, for his work to succeed. Blake saw the face of God, he saw the angels, could take these visions down on paper. Can we imagine the ridicule which would be heaped on such a man today? The artist is the eternal fool, close to the child and close to God."

This attitude towards art and life is an anodyne for the increasing sense of irrelevance in our modern world: We must go back to creative work and significant play, we must drop all empty substitutes, the adolescent thrills and games and gadgets which make us more lonely and more restless.

Eichenberg's prolific energy has taken him into other aspects of publishing. For twelve years he has edited *Artist's Proof,* a distinguished journal of prints and printmaking, published by the Pratt Graphics Center. He has written the encyclopedic *The Art of the Print,* published by Abrams, and *The Wood and the Graver,* a pictorial biography, published by Clarkson N. Potter. His prints have appeared freely and frequently in *The Catholic Worker,* published by his friend Dorothy Day.

In 1975–1976, Fritz Eichenberg began a new series of twenty woodblocks for a collection of short fables in verse, loosely based on the fables of Aesop, La Fontaine, and Fritz Eichenberg's own playful genius. These *Fables with a Twist* are droll gnomic tales told with a wry irony—mad and imaginative and magical parables about our common lot. Or as Fritz Eichenberg describes them, "The *Fables with a Twist* are old morals that have been turned around to fit our different times. They release pent-up worries about mankind's follies and the upside-down state of the world, and send out an appeal for sanity before the Final Blast."

Like Erasmus in *Praise of Folly*, Eichenberg tries to cover all of our misgivings about the dreadful problems of our time, such as corruption and hypocrisy and war, and like Erasmus he does so with a witty and graceful and urbane style.

The *Fables* are camouflaged to the extent that they do not point the finger at any recognizable personalities of our times; instead they hide their real meaning behind the animals who represent certain specific traits of human nature which are immediately recognizable. One Fable, "Total Disarmament," shows a Lamb presiding over a round conference table where there is a congregation of smiling wily beasts—a Snake, a Bear, a Crocodile, a Tiger, a Wolf, a Lion, and a Panther.

This fable is all the more powerful because Fritz Eichenberg is most well known throughout the world for his different prints of the *Peaceable Kingdom* vision of Isaiah 11:6:

The wolf shall dwell with the lamb, and the leopard shall lie down with the kid, and the calf and the lion and the fatling together, and a little child shall lead them.

This yearning for peace on earth is one of the oldest hungers of the human soul; from Isaiah to Erasmus to Eichenberg we have records of its appeal to the human conscience. But Snakes are not about to give up their fangs, and Lions are not about to give up their claws, and Tigers are not about to give up their teeth, and any Lamb that wanders into their midst and expects them to do so is asking to be eaten on the spot.

Isaiah and Erasmus and Eichenberg all know this, but, incurable Utopians that they are, they also all heartily wish that it might be otherwise—as their words and works testify.

New York City　　　　　　　　　　　　　　　　　　　*William Packard*
May 1979

The Ant & The Grasshopper

The Ant
and the Cricket

"Mind you," said Auntie Ant to Cousin Cricket,
"you are a parasite, a sponger, and a cheat
who dares to sing while others break their backs.
I warn you! Don't come knocking at my door
when old man Winter breezes down your neck,
and ask me for a handout. Out you go!"
And while the Ant began to stock her den
with the necessities for leaner days,
the Cricket sang!
Then winter came and howled around the house
and our busy Ant, quite snug and satisfied,
began to wait for that familiar knock
of Cousin Cricket, gaunt and woebegone.
It came one day, amidst a raging storm,
and with a smirk the Ant went to her door,
peeped through a crack and saw, aghast,
a beaming Cricket—longhaired, beaded, dressed
like Elvis Presley of the Insect World,
strumming on his guitar and singing loud:
"Hey, Auntie, take your duds, dress up, let's go
to gay Paree, with all expenses paid!
I was discovered by the Rolling Stones
who thought my songs were really out of sight—
gave me a contract, fifty grand a year,
London, New York, Berlin, next stop Paree!
Drop everything and be my wardrobe mistress.
Wake up and sing, my dear, let's live it up."
"How dare you," shrieked the Ant, "insult a maiden!
Out of my sight, corrupter of morale,
villain, who fiddles while I burn!
Fables be damned which just mislead the people!
But one thing you must do—for old times' sake:
Look up that vicious liar, La Fontaine
in Paris—ring the bell, and when he answers
grab his throat—and in my honest name
give him a beating that he won't forget!"
Says she—and slams the door.

The Vain Crow

A young and restless Crow got very tired
of always wearing black—the same old things.
One day, since garbage was her business,
she went through all the yards and city dumps
in search of something that might cheer her up.
Hurrah—what luck! To her immense delight
she found some peacock feathers, plastic flowers,
Christmas baubles, lots of other junk,
and happily she dressed before a broken mirror.
Since it was Easter morning she decided
to pay a flying visit to her rural friends.
Sensational! Did they jump on her?
Tear out her gaudy borrowed feathers?
No, no, they didn't! Off they went—
had their own treasure hunt, you bet,
searched trash and garbage dumps,
rushed home, dressed up, and had the best
Easter Parade within their memory!

the Sparrow and the Parrot

The Sparrow
and the Parrot

The good old days are gone!
Where horses once let drop their golden apples,
the motorcars spit out their filthy fumes,
and flocks of sparrows fight to make a living
round garbage cans and sanitation trucks.
Down at the heel, with ruffled feathers,
Mac Sparrow peeps into the living room
of a fine brownstone house on Sutton Place,
and sees, with grumbling stomach, big as life,
a splendid bird, perched in a gilded cage,
surrounded by the choicest seeds and cakes
that could delight a hungry sparrow's heart.
He hops across the marble window sill,
then wipes his dirty feet and gaily chirps:
"Hi, gov'nor! How's business? Can you spare
a seed for a poor fellow out of luck?
Or let me clean your cage? I need a job!"
His Honor blinks, and croaks: "Begone!
Got indigestion—ate too much last night—
sore throat—they made me talk all day—
arthritis I have in my joints and wings!
But after all—I am the only bird on earth
that owns a fourteen-carat golden cage.
Begone—I hate to see you fly around
since you remind me of the thing I miss—
my flying license!"

Endangered Species

Fritz Eichenberg

Endangered Species

The Eagle screeched—
the Rooster crowed—
the Dragon fumed—
but then the Lion roared:
"Enough!
For centuries we have suffered—
spread-eagled, shackled,
chained and crucified
on monstrous nations' coat-of-arms!
Oppressors all.
But I predict united we shall win!
We shall demand
eye for an eye and tooth for tooth
and royalties for all our royalty!
Justice we want for all injustices
inflicted on our vast constituency
throughout the world, back to Methuselah.
We'll fight it out with tooth and claw.
Mankind be damned—no quarter will be given.
Now it's their turn to take our place—
tarred, feathered, two-faced, double-headed monsters—
on all their shields, flags, infamous coat-of-arms.
War is declared herewith to that endangered species,
Homo sapiens! All those in favor? 'Aye!!!'
The motion carried—victory will be ours!"

total disarmament

Total Disarmament

Chairperson Lamb presiding, meek as ever,
at the last session of the Animals United
historic Conference on Peace on Earth,
Total Disarmament.
"This is an epoch-making moment," says the Lamb.
"These talks began five hundred years ago
when our ancestors decided, wisely so,
to do away with all agressive weapons!
The time has come to put the final seal
and signature on our solemn pact
never again to use fangs, teeth, or claws
on our brethren, be they weak or strong!
How many of these weapons we may need
for sustenance of life and its defense
has been discussed at length for many years.
The killing has to stop, the weapons have to go,
and peace will reign supreme in all the World.
I'll put it to the vote—all those in favor?"
All hell broke loose—no one to count the votes.
But the surviving council members all agreed:
they never feasted on a more delicious lunch
of leg of lamb and tender mutton chops
than at that last and definitely final session!

the Country and the City Mouse

Fritz Eichenberg

The Country
and the City Mouse

Sigmund, the City Mouse, geared to a life
of Culture, Comfort, exquisite Cuisine,
had cordially invited Cousin Elmer,
a country bumpkin living on a farm,
to visit him in his establishment.
And Elmer came, although quite ill at ease
since he had heard so much about a Cat
of formidable size and appetite,
well known as "Mac the Rodent Killer."
Surprise, surprise! As Elmer entered—
tip-toed into the sumptuous living room—
he saw stretched out as big as life
on the luxurious leather couch—yes—
Killer Mac, as peaceful as a kitten.
"You may not know, my friend,"
said Sigmund, blowing fragrant rings
from his Havana, "several years ago
I finished my degree (there on the wall)
in Paramutual Psychology.
Making a thorough study of this classic case,
I found that in her early pregnancy
Mac's mother had been scared, surprised
by a gigantic Mouse—and she, then he,
developed this hostility to our Race.
The rest was easy—Mac is happy now
on a strict Goldfish and Canary diet."

42

The Stock Market

43

The Stock Market

Stockholders' meeting in the Lion's Den—
big shots, small fries, and all the little proxies
hopefully voting this year's dividends.
Under the watchful eyes of Chairman Rex,
of Killem, Perish, Lynch and Pierce,
investment broker Shark, a deadly wit,
is looking for a victim of his tricks.
"Ah, Mister Primate," he begins his spiel,
"among these beasts you seem the only one
endowed with almost human comprehension.
With you a clever broker might discuss
stocks, bonds, tax-free securities,
and other pretty fascinating things.
Those Bulls and Bears bore me to tears—
I'd rather play the game with small investors.
I take their piggy banks and lead them by the nose,
I feed them tips, they grin and buy—
and usually end up as ham on rye.
Oh, how I love those tender little suckers!
I put the bite on them—then go in for the kill,
since in the end the sharpest teeth will win!
But listen—you are smarter than the lot—
would you be interested in a sure-fire deal
of which, by chance, I heard: Plutonium Limited,
a fabulous mine in darkest Africa?"

the New Adam

The New Adam

"The Evidence is Clear," thus spake the Lord
as He surveyed the Ruins of His Creation.
"I must confess: My Lack of Judgment
most logically to My Last Judgment leads—
unless I make amends for all My Grave Mistakes.
I must have been indeed dreadfully tired
when I created what undid this World."
"Adam and Eve," He mused, "the Apple, and the Fall
caused by the Snake. Eve lost her Innocence,
raised Cain—and I lost Patience.
The Deluge followed—poorly organized—
Child's Play compared with Man-Made Atom.
That Little World would have been better off
had I but turned it over to the Beasts."
"I will," said He in Wrath, and kicked a Star
that turned into a Comet right away,
"begin from Scratch, as I so blithely did
some foolish Hundred Billions Years ago—
except that now, by hindsight, I am wiser.
Mankind Be Damned, just as it damned itself
To Certain Final Hellish Liquidation!
This Being I create—I'll plan it well—
must have no Sex, nor must it ever think.
That, I am sure, is where the Evil starts.
Most certainly it must be deaf and dumb
and yet—it must be—let me think—
by far more powerful than Lightning
and faster than the Sound of Thunder.
It must be armorplated, bulletproof,
able to navigate on, over, under Land and Sea;
will need no Food or Fuel. I will see to that
with My Exclusive Patent, Solar Energy.
And I, the Lord, by all that's Holy
will run this Creature What's-Its-Name
with My Own Hands, completely by Computer!
So Be It—Sealed and Given
at My Celestial Executive Mansion,
in the New Year of Our Lord, One A."

The Bite

Eve had grown restless on a balmy day
in Paradise—no one to talk to but the Snake,
which, full of mischief, tried to sell the apple.
"How sweet it is!" he whispered in Eve's ear.
"Full of the juice of life, of tantalizing taste!"
"I had my fill of fruit," sweet Eve replied.
"But no forbidden one," so grinned the Snake,
"which will, with one small bite, reveal
the secret of creation, make you omnipotent,
all-knowing and all-seeing, like the Lord
who fashioned you, poor thing, from Adam's rib!"
"Stop," Adam shouted, "let me taste it first!
I have priority—I gave my best for you."
He grabbed the apple, sniffed it with delight,
opened his mouth . . . but here the animals,
endowed with common sense and insight,
began to yell and roar, to screech and bark:
"Don't touch the fruit of knowledge, so the Lord has said!
It's full of poison—you will hurt each other,
will lose your innocence, bear children with pain—
sweat, toil, and tears until Eternity!"
Too late! One heard the crunch of Adam's teeth,
the snake's triumphant laughter. In a flash,
the captain of the guard, with flaming sword,
expelled the pair—their crashing fall from grace.
And no return—no High Court of Appeal.
The bitter consequence: too many mouths to feed,
fights, jealousies, lawsuits and martyrdom
till Death, the Arbitrator, does them part forever.

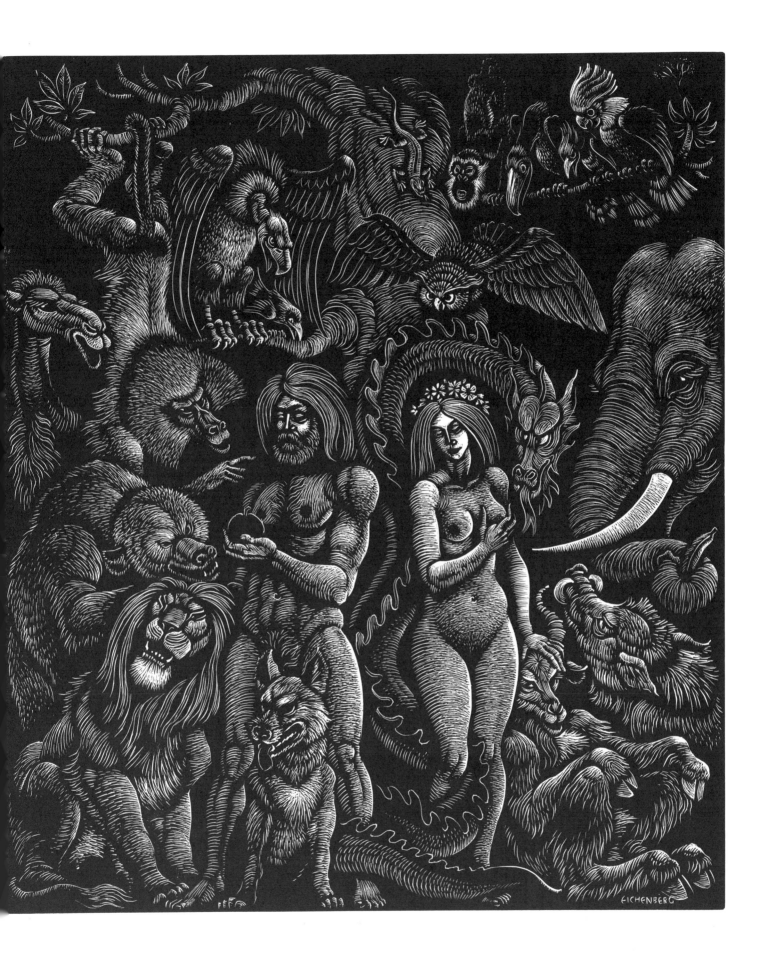

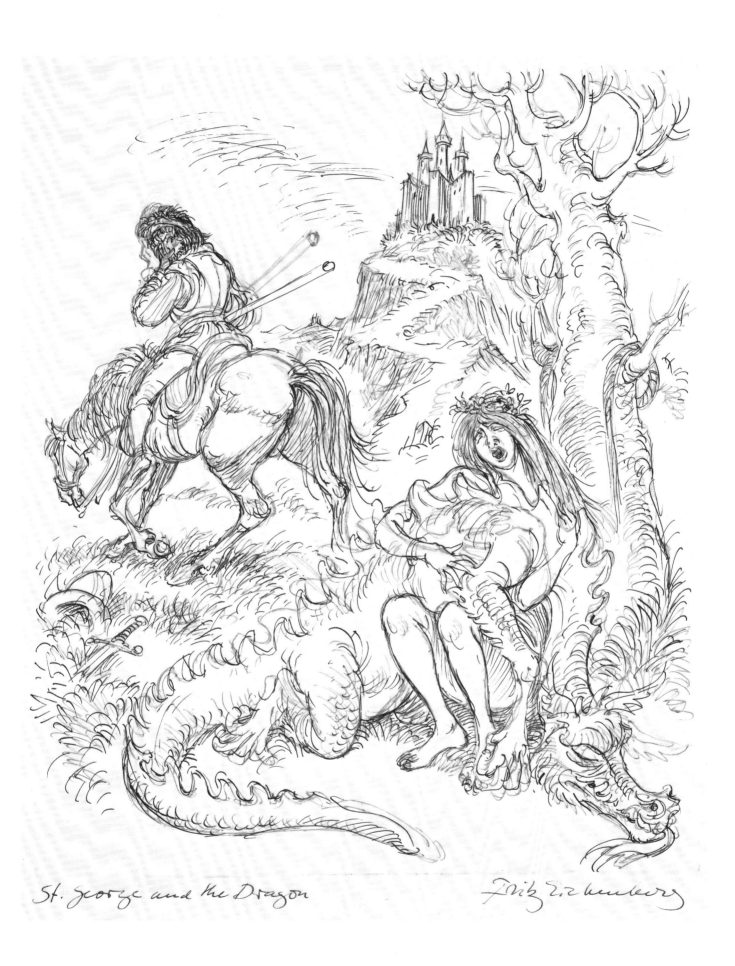

St. George and the Dragon

55

St. George and the Dragon

Compassionate St. George, the errant knight,
had heard some rumors of a dreadful dragon
who, for so many years, had terrorized
the humble people of the countryside.
The dragon, with his monstrous appetite,
had asked, as handsome ransom, every day
for breakfast, lunch or evening meal,
special delivery of a virtuous maiden.
St. George set out to find the dragon's lair,
and, in a lengthy, fearful, bloody battle,
he slew the ugly monster, freed the maid,
quite ready to receive the victor's spoil—
a kiss, a medal, or a laurel wreath.
Ah, what a shock! The distraught maiden
cursed George, her liberator, wept and moaned:
"My gallant lover, I would die for you!
How I will miss you, oh, my gentle friend!"
Puzzled St. George slunk off—a little wiser—
yet, as saintly fighters must,
ready to go into another battle.

The Shepherd & the Wolf

The Shepherd
and the Wolf

The shepherd boy was bored to tears.
There is no fun in counting sheep
from dawn to dusk and dusk to dawn
thinking of all the fun one missed.
He had cried "Wolf" just for the sport,
and got a hiding from his boss.
But then one day the Wolf appeared
all decked out in his Sunday best—
his teeth were glittering in the sun
as he surveyed the trembling sheep.
The shepherd boy, not scared one bit,
"Look here," he said to Brother Wolf.
"I need some dough for smokes and things
like flashy duds and fancy chicks.
Just say the word—I cut you in
on this here flock, we share the loot!"
The Wolf he grinned a toothy smile:
"Well said, my boy, here is my paw
and a bundle of dough in the bargain.
Cry 'Wolf' any time you need me, son,
or call me collect at my office!"
You want to know the happy end—
(not so, of course, for the poor sheep)?
The firm of Shepherd, Wolf, and Co
went public, prospered, and
paid handsome dividends
forever after!

The Donkey in the Lion Skin

The Donkey in the Lion Skin

"Underachiever, dropout, failure!"
So grumbled Donkey, who was getting old.
"What have I done but brayed my whole life long,
dragged heavy loads, and still
been beaten sore on top of everything.
But now for once," he swore,
"I want to be a Leader!"
As if by chance, he found a lion's skin,
and next to it a doorman's uniform,
complete with gold braid, medals, silver buttons.
Quickly he dressed, and gingerly stepped out
to show himself in all his pseudo-glory.
A gathering crowd of donkeys, overawed,
began to bray: "Hurray, We Want Our Leader!"
He raised his arm, gave them a proud salute,
bought them some guns, flags, uniforms,
and sent them off to fight. For what?
For Freedom From the Stick—
For More and Better Oats—
And Equal Loads for All.
It's odd that none of them came back!
But our Super Donkey, Duce, Leader,
he made himself—so people say—
Generalissimo and President-for-Life,
and soon retired on a handsome pension.

The Pied Piper of Hamelintown

The Pied Piper of Hamlintown

It's Halloween in Hamlintown—
who paid the Piper?
It's tricks and treats in Hamlintown—
who paid the Piper?
He'd promised death to rats and mice,
Peace to the People, candies to the kids,
but no one paid the Piper!
He shook his fist, vowed to return
to claim his fee, the great Exterminator.
It's Halloween again in Hamlintown—
who'll pay the Piper?
It's Tricks and Treats, and Rock and Roll—
who'll pay the Piper?
He's camouflaged in battle dress,
his flute it plays the sweetest tunes:
Of the rockets' red glare
and the Watch on the Rhine,
of allons enfants and comrades unite,
of down with and up with
and fight to the finish. . . .
It's Tricks and Treats for all the Kids
in Hamlintown,
and silence reigns supreme
in the ravine, the morning after.
Who paid the Piper?

69

70

The Blind Men and the Elephant   Fritz Eichenberg

The Blind Men and the Elephant

No living man—as far as we can tell—
has ever seen that splendid, fabled thing—
God, Idol, Monster—that we call
DE—MO—CRA—CY.
Some wise old men, though blind as bats,
but famous for their inner sight,
got a foundation grant to roam the world
through towns and cities, mountains, forests,
deserts and oceans—just to search for it.
And they, one day, right in the middle
of a dense jungle ran into a Thing
quite huge and solid, of tremendous size,
that roared and rumbled, yes,
and smelled and felt like this
strange fabled thing, DE—MO—CRA—CY.
"It's like a giant Broom to sweep the world,"
said number one.
"Methinks it's like a huge man-eating Snake,"
said number two.
"It's like a mighty Wall that nothing seems to shake,"
said number three.
"To me it seems more like a Sail before the storm,"
said number four.
"It's pointed like a Spear, I fear, a deadly weapon,"
said number five.
"To me . . . it's certainly . . . the biggest mountain . . . I have ever . . .
eeehhh," said number six, as he fell off.

the Wolf & the three little Kids

The Wolf
and the Three Little Kids

Who has not heard the tragic tale
of the dirty old Wolf with a special taste
for those tender underage little Kids,
and how he finally got them?
"Don't you ever open the door," Mom said,
"to any critter with teeth and claws,
no matter how sweet he talks," she said,
as she left for the late picture show.
But the Wolf he knew a trick or two
and he decked himself out with beads and guitar,
with long hair and a beard, of course,
as he knocked at the door of the little Kids' house.
"Just listen," he crooned, "to my latest smash,
number one on the Hit Parade!
Come, open the door and let's have some fun,
I am Jimmy the Beard, your old pal!"
When Mom returned they had flown the coop,
and the rest is history!
The Beard and the Kids are a howling success:
prime time on WKID-TV.
Tune in, dear reader, and see for yourself,
how it pays to trust a dirty old Wolf
with a taste for tender, innocent Kids,
and a nose for making a buck or two.

The Ballad of the World that Was

Fritz Eichenberg

The Ballad
of the World that Was

It's hard to say which year it was
the clocks had stopped,
time had run out.
The Holocaust had come and gone—
No enemies were left to fight
and Peace was hiding in the ruins.
If there'd been left some ears to listen,
they could have heard a tiny sound,
a tinkle from a little hurdy-gurdy—
the stomping of a foot,
a monkey's chattering—
an organ grinder!
Some chords were missing, but it seems
the melody was familiar:
"Oh, say can you see . . .
by the dawn's early light . . ."
Too bad there were no eyes to see
nor hands to give a penny to the monkey,
as our last survivor,
slightly out of tune,
ground out the Ballad of a World
That Was—but no one cared to listen.

The Lion and the Mouse

The Lion
and the Mouse

Leo, the King of Beasts, trapped in a net!
You must have heard this most exciting story,
how freedom he had granted to a little mouse
who, I suspect, had been a bit too small
for this great Majesty's tremendous appetite.
Now when she saw him caught in this dilemma,
the mouse proved to be more cunning than a fox.
"I'll spare your precious life, your Majesty,
as you spared mine!" She bowed and smiled
and called collect long distance Barnum-Bailey,
drew up an airtight contract with a clause
that gave the Mouse Humane Society
(of which she was the Treasurer-Secretary)
fifty percent of all the tickets sold
for Royal Leo's Death-defying Act—
shot from a cannon (hold your breath)
into a barrel filled with ice-cold water!
Poor Leo groaned—and signed—was carted off
to the Big Top—fit to be tied!

After the Blast

After the Blast

The End had come. The world was laid to waste
by one last man-made cataclysmic blast.
Mankind, beast, reptile, fish and fowl,
turned into ashes—gone to their reward.
Peace, after all, had come, and silence reigned supreme
on land and sea.
Millenia have passed—
nature has mercifully healed the scars,
has clothed the hills and vales in luscious green,
and in some hidden caves one hears a whisper,
scratching of tiny feet, a rustling of wings.
A race of hardy insects has survived the blast,
calls an assembly, and seems well prepared
to reestablish the Establishment.
Chairperson by concensus, Reverend Mother
the Praying Mantis, gives the invocation:
"We thank thee, Master of the Universe,
for having freed us of the human race,
a plague of unbelievable dimensions.
Having survived their poisons, traps and fumes,
we have achieved sufficient stamina
to rule the world. We are the Master Race!
All power to the Insect!"
Here she bangs the gavel.
"Let us proceed," she says, "to draft a constitution,
based on nonviolence, equality of sex.
No bites or stings except for peaceful use,
no slavery, and, of course, a vegetarian diet—"
Here some voices rise, and angry cries are heard:
"Out with the pious one! She ate her husband!
Let's put the Bee on her! Long live the Queen!"
Her Majesty the Bee ascends the rostrum:
"My fellow subjects! No great monarchy
could possibly survive without the help

of its great labor force, its woman-power,
ceaselessly working without pay. . . ."
A howl goes up: "We don't want slavery!
Down with the Queen, up with the workingman
who uses head and hands. Let's get the Spider!"
Between two trees the Spider spins his nct.
"Your vote of confidence is all I need!"
he grins, and grabs a juicy fly.
"Out with the rascal!" buzz her fellow flies.
"Don't you remember? No more meat for you!"
"Whom are we getting now? Beauty without a sting,
the Butterfly!" The audience claps and cheers
and catches the Admiral. "Careful!" he lisps,
"my wings are fragile—please don't touch!
I live on dew, flutter from rose to rose—
so sorry, kind of restless, can't stay long,"
and takes his leave among some boos and hisses.
The latest candidate considered is the Flea.
"At least," some voters say, "he'll keep us hopping."

91

The Ark of Love

The Ark of Love

The Ark of Love

The good ship Ark, a manifest of love,
set out to sea upon the Lord's command.
The rains came down, and mankind's sins
were drowned by all the raging waters.
"Take two of every kind," the Lord had said,
"of all the innocent creatures of the Earth,
and give them shelter, care and nourishment
so that they may survive and multiply."
Noah, the navigator, sailed the Seven Seas
until the dove returned, with olive branch
found on dry land above the sinking waters.
The Lord be praised.
The Ark, according to the Master's plan,
when safely landed on Mount Ararat,
disgorged the cargo of its joyful creatures,
who spread across the Earth, and multiplied.
What happened since defies imagination.
Headlines proclaim: Exploded populations—
oceans polluted—wars and genocide—
animal kingdom threatened with extinction.
Sodom? Gomorrah? Surely model cities!
Committees charged with finding facts
about the deluge's dismal failure
offered this sorry hindsight explanation:
The Lord made a mistake!
Instead of Noah, he should have appointed
the crocodile as captain of the Ark—
and Peace would reign supreme on land and sea.

the Donkey and the Lapdog

Fritz Eichenberg

The Donkey
and the Lapdog

The Donkey, so the story goes,
quite jealous of the Lapdog's privilege,
one day decided he must try his luck.
He rushed into the room
onto his mistress' lap—
he licked her face—
locked her in his embrace—
What happened? No disgrace?
No cry for help? Good Lord,
it seems she liked it!

Isaiah's Riddle

Isaiah's Riddle

Peaceable Kingdom was a prophet's dream
of a new world, Utopia,
where swords are beaten into plowshares,
where the strong protect the weak,
and lions learn to love the lambs
not for their tender meat—
where ox and bear will form alliances
and wolves forego the pleasure of the hunt.
A little child will lead them,
playing with a snake
whose bite she does not fear.
Where do we find this Kingdom, wise Isaiah?
The answer comes across millenia,
a sigh so faint:
"Search, search for it, make haste,
It's buried in your own heart, mind, and soul."

ISAIAH II ✡ FRITZ EICHENBERG 1976

Godfather of the Rock

Fritz Eichenberg

Godfather
of the Rock

Orpheus, Godfather of the Rock,
Son of the Muse, divine Calliope!
Such was the power of his rhymes and songs
that he could move rocks, men and beasts
to utter ecstasy and wild abandon.
Alas, it hurts to contemplate his dreadful end.
He lost his wife, the nymph Euridice,
by looking back at her in Hades' underworld.
And then, so goes the sad and ancient tale,
for losing interest in both life and women,
Orpheus was torn to pieces by the jealous Maenads.
His head and lyre, floating down to sea,
were buried on the famous Isle of Lesbos.
Beware, ardent disciples of the Rock,
of these extreme vocational hazards,
against which, as we know for sure,
no Lloyd's of London or of ancient Athens
would ever care to underwrite insurance.

Bullfrog for President

Fritz Eichenberg

Bullfrog
For President

One day a bullfrog, living in a pond
quite lonely, practicing his voice,
observed a herd of thirsty bulls
bellowing to their hearts' content
as they came in for their evening drink.
"Now I'll show them a thing," thought Bully the Frog.
"I'll blow myself up if I bust"—
and he opened his mouth as wide as he could
and he blew himself up to twice his size
and he croaked as no one had croaked before.
He kicked up a storm in that little pond
and stopped the bulls dead in their tracks.
They never had heard such a mighty song
and it knocked them right off their feet.
"Hip, hip, hurray for the Super Bull!"
they yelled as they carried him off,
and they made him run for President
of the Grand Old Bulls' Federation.
He won, dear folks, by common consent,
on a Bull-Frog bipartisan ticket.

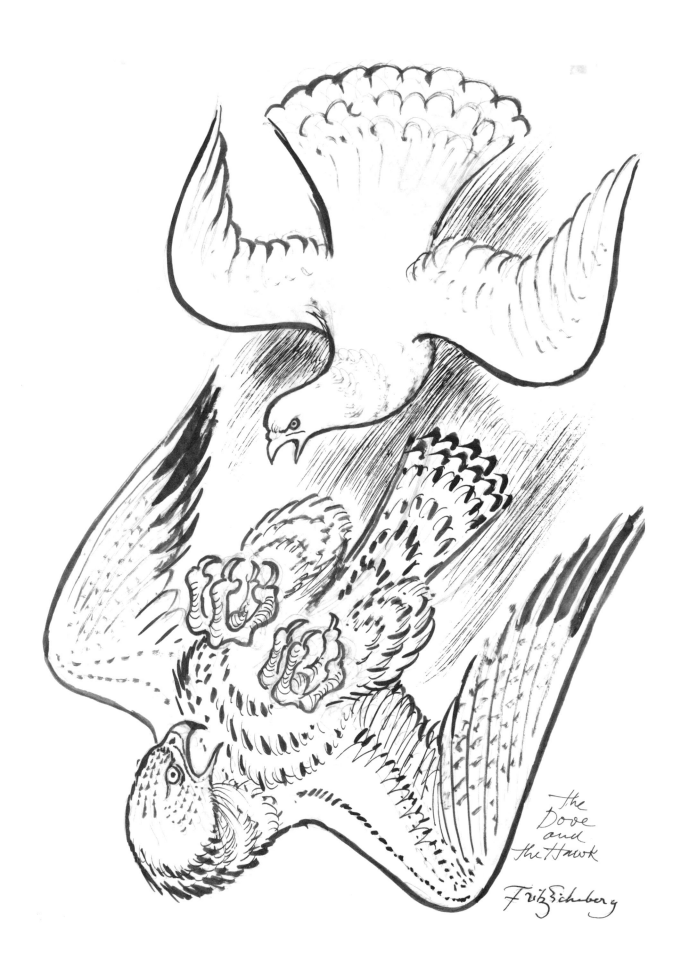

the
Dove
and
the Hawk

Fritz Eichenberg

The Dove
and the Hawk

The fearful Hawk,
Not having heard of that Old-Kingdom
Pax Vobiscum,
had ruled the skies for centuries
with great impunity.
He'd had a license to hunt pigeons
since time began.
What fun! They always turned
the other cheek.
Until the day, to his surprise,
the Hawk met Super-Dove.
She'd heard of Joan of Arc,
dive-bombed the mighty bird,
and won the fight—
and immortality.

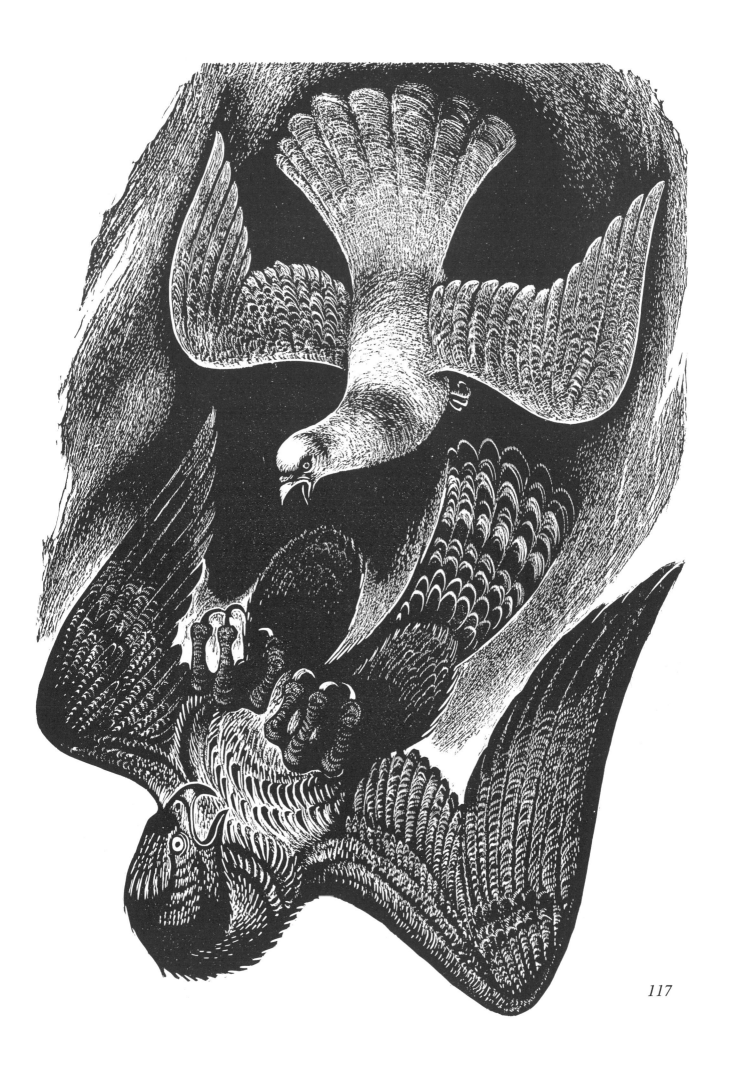

117

The Night Watch   Fritz Eichenberg

Nightwatch

Midnight has fallen
and the woods are quiet.
Truce has been declared,
the hunt has stopped.
The eagle has his fill,
the gulls are resting,
and the fish
are safely sleeping in their pond.
The pigeon dreams of love,
the crow of sharing carrion
with the vulture.
The owl is wide awake.
The watchman of the night
must think of weightier things
than mice.
Pallas Athena's bird, with a degree
in wisdom, perches on a skull
and ponders what those eggs may yield:
New insights, a messiah,
or new horrors—
perhaps a neutron bomb?

The Peaceable Tree   Fritz Eichenberg

The Peaceable Tree

A tree was dreaming—so the fable goes—
of pulling up its roots to see the world,
of which the owl had told him many stories.
He knew that birds can fly, that beasts can run,
and climb and jump from branch to branch.
The humans he had seen walked on two legs
or raced along on wheels—like lunatics.
"Yet," said the owl, an avid TV viewer
peeking through nightly windows,
"people are always talking about roots.
They search for them, write books about them,
travel long distances to dig them up,
are proud of them, like knights of their escutcheons."
The tree was listening with rapt attention:
"I thank you, owl, as always, for your counsel;
you have convinced me that my dreams are wrong.
Woodpeckers knock me, squirrels annoy me
by hiding nuts in knotholes.
Old branches ache, drop off in heavy snow,
and storms sweep through my crown.
Yet spring will come, and little leaves
will sprout and rustle in the breeze.
Just as you say, the root's the thing!
I think I'll stay—
and sink them just a little deeper!"

Biographical Notes

Fritz Eichenberg was born in Cologne, Germany, where he first studied at the School of Applied Arts, and then served as a lithographic apprentice at the publishing house of DuMont Schauberg, before being accepted as a master student by Professor Steiner-Prag at the Academy of Graphic Arts in Leipzig.

Moving to Berlin in 1923, he became a roving reporter and staff artist for the Ullstein Publishing House, until Hitler came to power in 1933. In that year the artist decided to start a new life in the United States, at the height of the Great Depression.

At first he taught at the New School for Social Research in New York, worked on the Federal Art Project, did political cartoons for the *Nation,* and illustrated children's books.

Then came the first important commissions from the Limited Editions Club and the Heritage Press. With wood engravings and lithographs, his favorite media, he illustrated many of the great classics by Dostoevsky and Tolstoy, Turgenev and Pushkin, Swift and Shakespeare.

He became well known for his prints and illustrations, executed for new editions of Edgar Allan Poe, *Wuthering Heights* and *Jane Eyre* by the Brontës, the stories of Dylan Thomas and Wilkie Collins, and most recently, in 1979, Grimmelshausen's *The Adventurous Simplicissimus*.

Many of these prints are now in the permanent collections of the Library of Congress, the National Gallery, the Metropolitan Museum of Art, Yale University Library, the Hermitage, the Vatican, the Bibliothèque Nationale and many other important public and private collections throughout the world.

Fritz Eichenberg began teaching at Pratt Institute in 1947. While there, he served as chairman of the Art Department, and as director of the Pratt Graphics Center. He also acted as editor-in-chief of *Artist's Proof,* a journal on printmaking, and founded the ADLIB Press.

In 1966 he moved to Rhode Island as chairman of the Art Department of the University in Kingston, a position he held until 1971. He has traveled extensively in semi-official capacities, to the USSR for the State Department and to Southeast Asia for the

J.D.R.III Fund. Four honorary degrees of Doctor of Fine Arts were conferred upon him between 1972 and 1978.

Most recently he has written a definitive work on the graphic arts, *The Art of the Print,* published by Harry N. Abrams, Inc., and a monograph, *The Wood and the Graver,* published by Clarkson N. Potter, Inc.

Several large portfolios of prints have been published over the years: Erasmus' *In Praise of Folly,* a collection of his own fables, and engravings for the Old Testament.

William Packard, founder and editor of *New York Quarterly,* is a professor at the Washington Square Writing Center of New York University, where he conducts the poetry-writing workshops. He teaches poetry at various city schools and universities, and playwriting at the HB Studio in Manhattan. He is director of the New York City Writers Conference at Wagner College, co-director of the Hofstra Writers Conference, and the Padraic Colum Lecturer at the Suffield Writer-Reader Conference.

Endangered Species

Designed by Antonie Eichenberg
Composed by the Maryland Linotype Composition Company
in Times Roman display and text
Color separations by Capper, Inc., Knoxville, Tennessee
Printed by A. Colish, Inc., Mount Vernon, New York,
on 80 pound Mohawk Superfine Softwhite Smooth paper
Bound in Buckram/Record Natural Finish cloth
by Delmar Printing Company, Charlotte, North Carolina
Bound in paper by Bindagraphics, Inc., Baltimore, Maryland